ALSO FROM JOE BOOKS

Disney 101 Dalmatians Cinestory Comic
Disney•Pixar Comics Treasury
Disney Big Hero 6 Cinestory Comic
Disney•Pixar Inside Out Cinestory Comic
Disney Gravity Falls Cinestory Comic Volume One
Disney Gravity Falls Cinestory Comic Volume Two
Disney Gravity Falls Cinestory Comic Volume Three
Disney•Pixar The Good Dinosaur Cinestory Comic
Disney Zootopia Cinestory Comic
Disney Winnie the Pooh Cinestory Comic
Disney Alice in Wonderland Cinestory Comic
Disney•Pixar Finding Nemo Cinestory Comic
Disney•Pixar Finding Dory Graphic Novel
Disney Zootopia Graphic Novel
Disney Darkwing Duck Comics Collection Volume One
Disney Moana Comics Collection

Don't miss our monthly comics…
Disney Frozen
Disney Pirates of the Caribbean
Disney Princess
Disney Star vs the Forces of Evil

Disney · PIXAR

FINDING DORY

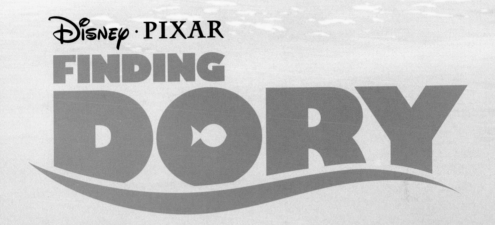

CINESTORY COMIC

JOE BOOKS LTD

Published in the United States and Canada by Joe Books Ltd
489 College Street, Suite 203, Toronto, Ontario, M6G 1A5.

www.joebooks.com

First Joe Books Edition: May 2017

Print ISBN: 978-1-77275-482-7
ebook ISBN: 978-1-77275-298-4

Library and Archives Canada Cataloguing in Publication
information is available upon request.

Printed and bound in Canada
1   3   5   7   9   10   8   6   4   2

"HI, I'M DORY."

I SUFFER FROM SHORT-TERM REMEMBERY LOSS.

YES!

THAT'S *EXACTLY* WHAT YOU SAY.

OKAY, OKAY. WE'LL PRETEND TO BE THE OTHER KIDS NOW.

HUUHH

AHEM

HI, DORY.

AHOY THERE!

GIGGLE

DO YOU WANT TO PLAY HIDE-AND-SEEK?

OKAY!

TEE HEE!

WE'LL HIDE, AND YOU COUNT AND COME FIND US.

OKAY, DADDY.

I LIKE SAND. SAND IS SQUISHY.

HA HA HA!

HA HA HA!

⌐GASP¬ MOMMY, CAN I GO PLAY WITH THEM?

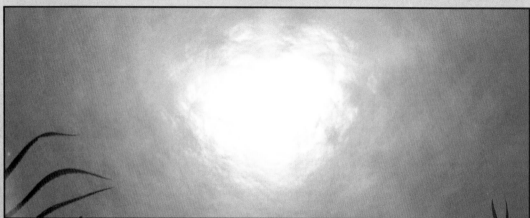

HELLO?

BUT DORY IS GONE.

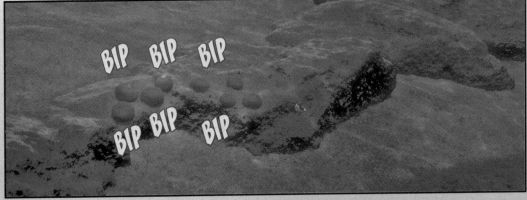

TIME PASSES...

HI, I'VE LOST MY FAMILY. CAN YOU HELP ME?

WHERE DID YOU SEE THEM LAST?

WELL...UHH. FUNNY STORY, BUT, UH...I *FORGOT*.

OH, SWEETIE... DO YOU WANT TO COME SWIM WITH US?

THAT IS THE NICEST OFFER I'VE GOTTEN ALL DAY... I THINK. UGH. I CAN'T REMEMBER. ANYHOO-- THANKS, BUT I'M LOOKING FOR SOMEONE.

OO--OH... CAN'T REMEMBER, CAN'T REMEMBER, CAN'T REMEMBER...

MORE TIME PASSES...

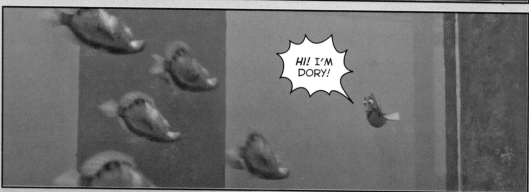

HI! I'M DORY!

WAS IT SOMETHING I SAID? KIDDING. OKAY, OKAY... YOU'RE NOT COMING BACK.

FWSSH

I WAS LOOKING FOR SOMETHING AND I--

OKAY. TOTALLY GET IT. DATE NIGHT. HAVE FUN!

HUH?

A WHITE BOAT! THEY TOOK MY SON! *MY SON!* HELP ME! PLEASE!

THE TWO FISH COLLIDE, SENDING BOTH SPRAWLING...

AGH!

⋛UNGH!⋜

WHUD

⋛NGH!⋜

THUD

22

one year later

ZZZZZZZZ.
KLAUS? KLAUS,
THE PIÑATA'S
DROOPING.

I NEED A
RATCHET
WRENCH...I
CAN FIX IT...

BUMP

OW.

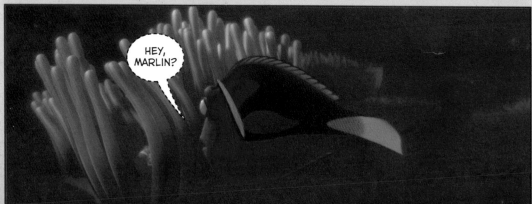

HEY, MARLIN?

zzzZZzzz...

ZZZZZZT

﹈SIGH﹈
HEY, GUYS I
WAS JUST--

OW-OW-
OW-OW!

BACK TO BED. THAT WAS IT. VERY SIMPLE. BED. BACK TO IT.

AH. MM-HMM, GOT IT.

HEY, MARLIN--

÷YAWN÷

AND WE'RE UP. THAT'S IT. READY TO START THE DAY.

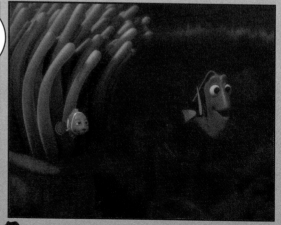

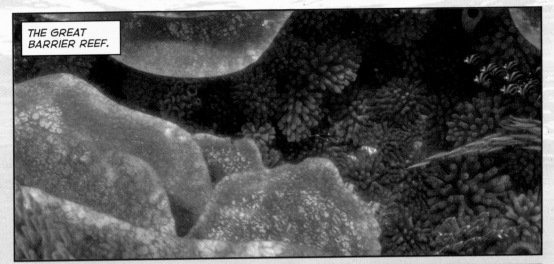

THE GREAT BARRIER REEF.

NEMO.

AND WE WERE LOOKING FOR SOMETHING.

RIGHT! I REMEMBER IT LIKE IT WAS YESTERDAY. OF COURSE, I DON'T REALLY REMEMBER YESTERDAY ALL THAT WELL.

ANYWAY, I WOULD SAY THE SCARIEST MOMENT OF THE TRIP WAS THE FOUR SHARKS.

:GIGGLE:

WAIT, I THOUGHT THERE WERE *THREE* SHARKS.

NO. NO, THERE WERE *DEFINITELY* FOUR.

BUT LAST TIME YOU TOLD IT, THERE WERE THREE.

SON, WHICH ONE OF US TRAVELED ACROSS THE ENTIRE OCEAN?

NEMO DID.

WAH!

OBVIOUSLY WE HAD TO CROSS THE OCEAN TO FIND HIM, SO YOU KNOW...HE WENT FIRST.

I GUESS THAT'S TRUE. ISN'T IT?

UH... NO, NOT EXACTLY.

WELL, I AM SO HONORED. I HAVE NEVER BEEN A TEACHING ASSISTANT BEFORE.

⸫SIGH⸫

MR. RAY! YOU GOT HELP.

OOOOOOHHH... OKEY DOKEY!

DORY!

GOOD QUESTION, GOOD QUESTION. SEE, I CAN REMEMBER SOME THINGS BECAUSE--WELL, UH...THEY JUST MAKE SENSE. LIKE, UM...WELL I HAVE A FAMILY. I KNOW BECAUSE I...Y'KNOW, I MUST HAVE COME FROM SOMEWHERE, RIGHT?

EVERYONE HAS A FAMILY. I MAY NOT REMEMBER THEIR NAMES, AND WHAT THEY LOOK LIKE, AND I MAY NOT EVEN BE ABLE TO FIND THEM AGAIN, BUT, UM...

WHAT WERE WE TALKING ABOUT?

MOMMIES AND DADDIES.

THAT'S WHAT AN *INSTINCT* IS, NEMO. SOMETHING DEEP INSIDE YOU THAT FEELS SO FAMILIAR THAT YOU HAVE TO LISTEN TO IT...

...LIKE A SONG YOU'VE ALWAYS KNOWN!

AND I CAN HEAR MINE NOW!

SUDDENLY, THE UNDERTOW CREATED BY THE RAYS PULLS DORY INTO THEIR PARADE!

AAH!

DORY!

AAAAH!

DORY'S MIND FLASHES BACK TO A DISTANT MEMORY...

DOOOOORRRYY!

...THEN ALL GOES BLACK AND SILENT, BUT FOR A DISTANT VOICE...

"THE JEWEL OF MORRO BAY, CALIFORNIA!"

GASP!

DORY REMEMBERS, IN A SUDDEN FLASH OF IMAGES...

MARINE LIFE INSTITUTE

THE ONLY REASON TO TRAVEL IN THE FIRST PLACE IS SO YOU DON'T HAVE TO TRAVEL EVER AGAIN!

YEAH, BUT I WANT TO--

PLEASE. ALL I KNOW... IS THAT I MISS THEM.

I REALLY, REALLY MISS THEM. I DIDN'T KNOW WHAT THAT FELT LIKE. DO YOU KNOW WHAT THAT FEELS LIKE?

AND NOW WE'RE LOOKING FOR MY PARENTS AT THE "BROOCH OF THE ATLANTIC?" OR THE--

THE JEWEL OF MORRO BAY, CALIFORNIA!

EXACTLY!

HOW ARE YOU GOING TO FIND YOUR PARENTS?

DO YOU REMEMBER WHAT THEY LOOK LIKE?

I'M A BIT NEW TO THE MEMORY THING, SO I CAN'T SAY FOR SURE, BUT SOMETHING TELLS ME THEY WERE MOSTLY BLUE, WITH MAYBE... YELLOW?

THAT SOUNDS RIGHT.

ALSO, I'M PRETTY SURE I'M GONNA KNOW THEM WHEN I SEE THEM. WE'RE *FAMILY*.

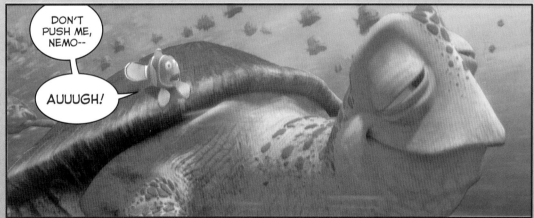

-:GASP:-

JENNY AND CHARLIE.

WHAT? JENNY AND WHAT...?

THOSE ARE THEIR NAMES. MY PARENTS ARE *JENNY AND CHARLIE!*

JENNY?! CHARLIE?! JENNY?! CHARLIE?!

DORY! DORY, STOP YELLING FOR A SECOND! IT'S NOT A GOOD IDEA TO COME INTO A NEW NEIGHBORHOOD AND CALL THIS MUCH ATTENTION TO YOURSELF!

YOU DON'T UNDERSTAND, I REMEMBERED MY PARENTS' NAMES.

JENNY! CHARLIE!

SHHHH!

DORY, DORY, DORY, THESE CRABS ARE LOCALS, AND I GET THE FEELING THEY'RE SHUSHING US FOR A REASON.

YOU MIGHT WAKE UP SOMETHING *DANGEROUS.*

ARE YOU TALKING ABOUT, LIKE, SOMETHING WITH ONE BIG EYE, TENTACLES, AND A SNAPPY THING?

WELL, THAT'S VERY *SPECIFIC,* BUT SOMETHING LIKE THAT, YES. YOU JUST IN GENERAL DON'T WANT TO--

MARLIN, NEMO, AND DORY SWIM AWAY AS FAST AS THEIR FINS CAN CARRY THEM, PURSUED BY THE GIANT SQUID!

AAAH!

WHOOOAAAA! WHOA! SWIM FOR YOUR LIFE!

THE TRIO SWIMS THROUGH AN OLD SHIPPING CONTAINER...

...GETTING TANGLED IN A SIX-PACK RING, THE SQUID IN HOT PURSUIT!

AAAAARGH!

THOOM

DORY, MARLIN AND NEMO RACE AHEAD, TOWARD THE SUNKEN SHIP AND ITS SHIPPING-CONTAINER CARGO...

AAAAAH!

AAAAH!

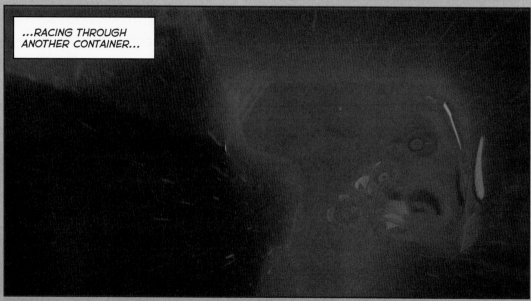

...RACING THROUGH ANOTHER CONTAINER...

...AND OUT THE OTHER SIDE, THROUGH AN OPENING TOO NARROW FOR THE PURSUING SQUID!

WAAAAUGH!

THE WEIGHT OF THE STRUGGLING SQUID IS TOO MUCH FOR THE PRECARIOUSLY BALANCED CONTAINER, AND IT BEGINS TO FALL...

...BUT ONE TENTACLE LASHES OUT...

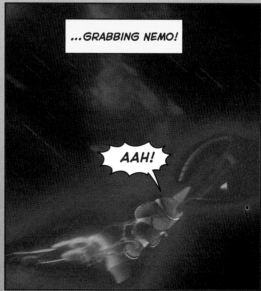

...GRABBING NEMO!

AAH!

NEMO!

NEMO!

DAD! DAD!

THOOM

THE SQUID BEGINS TO PULL NEMO TOWARD ITS SNAPPING MOUTH!

NO! AAAAH!

NEMO, HOLD ON TO ME! AND *DON'T LET GO!*

STILL TUMBLING, THE CONTAINER TIPS END OVER END...

CRASH

...FINALLY COMING TO REST...

...ON *TOP* OF THE TERRIFYING SQUID!

BA-BOOM!

FREE OF THE SQUID, DORY SWIMS FRANTICALLY...

⋟HUFF HUFF⋞

DORY! *DORY!*

⋟HUFF HUFF⋞

DORY, *SLOW DOWN!* WE'RE NOT BEING CHASED ANYMORE!

ARE YOU SURE?!

BUMP

AAH!

JENNY... JENNY AND CHARLIE... JENNY AND CHARLIE!

I-I JUST REMEMBERED THEIR NAMES! WE HAVE TO KEEP GOING--WE'RE SO CLOSE!

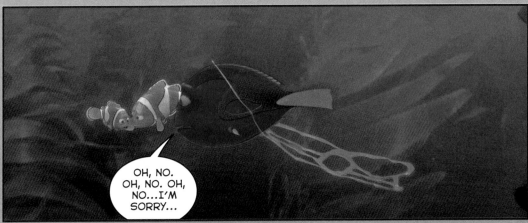

...I HAVE?

OH, NO. BUT I--I CAN FIX IT. I CAN. I-I'LL GO GET HELP--

YOU KNOW WHAT YOU CAN DO, DORY? YOU CAN GO WAIT OVER THERE. GO WAIT OVER THERE AND *FORGET.*

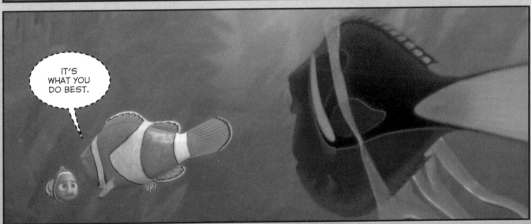

IT'S WHAT YOU DO BEST.

YOU'RE RIGHT. I DON'T KNOW WHY I THOUGHT I COULD DO THIS...FIND MY FAMILY... I CAN'T DO THIS. I'M SO SORRY, I'LL FIX IT.

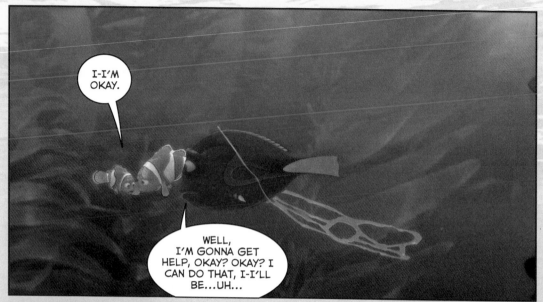

I-I'M OKAY.

WELL, I'M GONNA GET HELP, OKAY? OKAY? I CAN DO THAT, I-I'LL BE...UH...

IT'LL BE ALL RIGHT, NEMO!

HELLO? SOMEONE? HELLO?

DORY SWIMS DEEPER INTO THE KELP...

ANYONE? HELLO? ANYONE?

...SUDDENLY, A VOICE ECHOES FROM ABOVE...

HELLO.

VRRRRRRRRMMMMMM

DON'T WORRY, DORY! STAY CALM! WE'LL COME FIND YOU!

EXPERIENCE OCEAN LIFE... AS THEY DO.

MARINE LIFE INSTITUTE

AND WELCOME TO THE MARINE LIFE INSTITUTE, WHERE WE BELIEVE IN RESCUE, REHABILITATION, AND RELEASE.

MARINE LIFE INSTITUTE

MARLIN! NEMO!

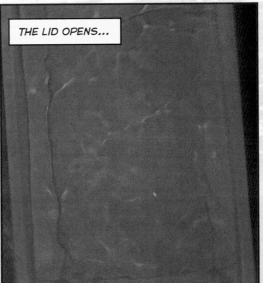

THE LID OPENS...

SPLOOSH

...AND DORY IS UNCEREMONIOUSLY DROPPED INTO A TANK!

GASP

HUFF HUFF

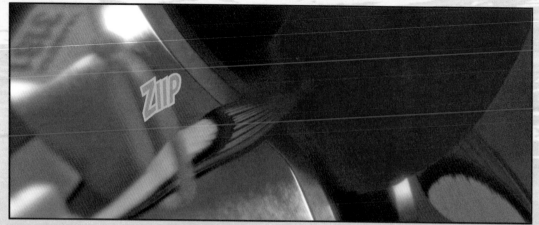

DORY IS CLIPPED WITH A TAG.

ZIIP

KLAK

LOOKS LIKE WE'RE DONE HERE.

DUDE, CUT IT OUT. YOU'RE A SCIENTIST. WE TALKED ABOUT THIS.

OH, C'MON. IT'S FUNNY.

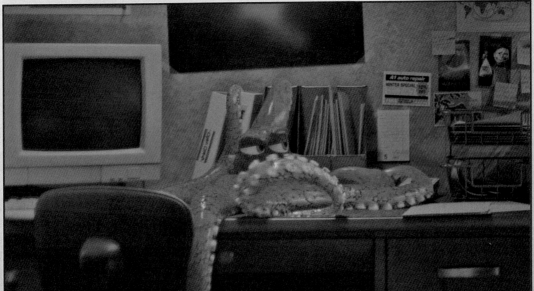

OH BOY...

OKAY, OKAY, OKAY, THIS IS...

SLUP

...I'LL BE FINE. I JUST NEED TO FIND A WAY OUT AND AH...JUST...

SHWIP

...GET A HOLD OF YOURSELF, GET A HOLD OF YOURSELF...

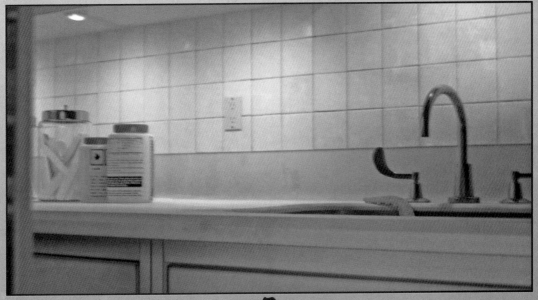

KLAK

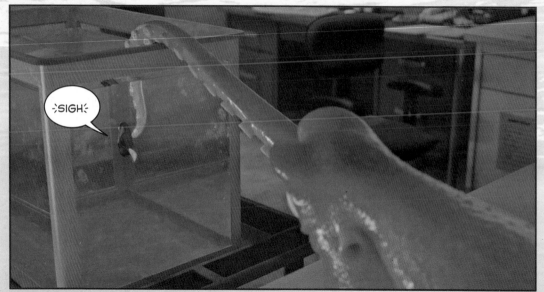

IN CLEVELAND.

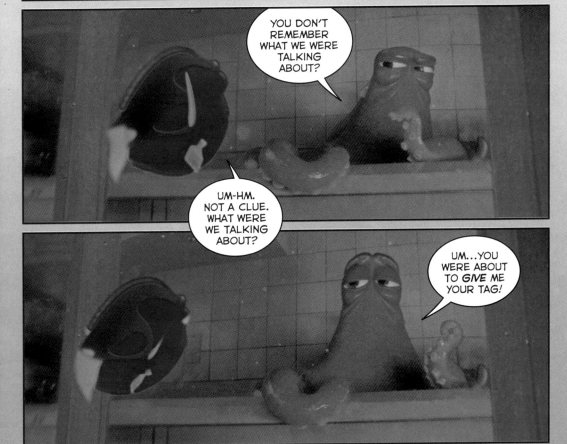

CLEVELAND? HM. I HEAR GOOD THINGS ABOUT CLEVELAND. WHY DO YOU WANT TO GO?

BECAUSE, IF I STAY *HERE,* I'M GONNA GET RELEASED BACK TO THE OCEAN! AND I HAVE EXTREMELY UNPLEASANT MEMORIES OF THAT PLACE! ⸬SIGH⸬ I JUST WANT TO LIVE IN A GLASS BOX ALONE. IT'S ALL I WANT!

SO *GIVE* ME YOUR *TAG!*

HEY, MAN, DON'T TOUCH MY TAG.

SLAP

⸬SIGH⸬

LOOK.

ARE YOU ABSOLUTELY SURE THAT'S WHAT I SAID? "GO WAIT OVER THERE AND FORGET. IT'S WHAT YOU DO BEST!"?

YEAH, DAD.

I SAID *THAT?*

YOU SAID THAT, DORY SWAM TO THE SURFACE, AND THEN SHE GOT TAKEN BY SOME--

ALL RIGHT, I DON'T NEED THE WHOLE STORY AGAIN--I WAS ASKING ABOUT ONE PART. BECAUSE, LOOK, IF I SAID THAT, AND I'M NOT POSITIVE I *DID,* IT-IT'S ACTUALLY A COMPLIMENT. BECAUSE I ASKED HER TO WAIT. AND I SAID IT'S WHAT YOU DO *BEST.* SO, I-I--

OH, IT'S MY FAULT. IT'S ALL MY FAULT DORY GOT KIDNAPPED AND TAKEN INTO-- WHATEVER THIS PLACE IS! WHAT IF IT'S A *RESTAURANT?!*

GERALD!! GET OFF THE ROCK! GET OFF!

NOW YOU KNOW BETTER!

OFF! OFF! OFF! OFF! OFF!--

OY! GERALD! SHOVE OFF, GERALD! COME ON! GO ON!

OFF! OFF! OFF! OFF!--

SPLOOSH

OFF! OFF! OFF! OFF!

DON'T YOU WORRY ABOUT A THING. THAT PLACE IS THE MARINE LIFE INSTITUTE-- THE JEWEL OF MORRO BAY, CALIFORNIA.

:-SIGH-:

MOMMY...

PURPLE SHELLS! PURPLE SHE--HANK, MY HOME HAD A *PURPLE SHELL!*

SO WHAT? HALF THE EXHIBITS HERE HAVE PURPLE SHELLS IN THEM!

NO, NO, NO...YOU DON'T UNDERSTAND! I REMEMBER HER NOW! PURPLE SHELLS WERE HER *FAVORITE!* AND SHE HAD THIS ADORABLE GIGGLE. AND THEN MY DAD WAS REALLY FRIENDLY...

:-GASP!-:

AND NOW YOUR WACKY MEMORY'S GONNA GET US **CAUGHT.**

HANK GOES DOWN THE HALL AND THROUGH A DOOR, BUT THE STAFFER IS HEADED THE SAME WAY!

GIVING UP ON THE SEARCH FOR THE MISSING OCTOPUS, THE STAFFER PICKS UP THE BUCKET.

HANK FOLLOWS AS FAST AS HE CAN.

⇥HNGH!⇤

⇥HUFF HUFF⇤

⇥NNGH!⇤

SUDDENLY, A STAFFER'S HAND PLUNGES INTO THE BUCKET AND TOSSES DORY INTO...

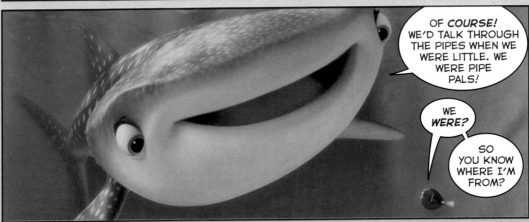

131

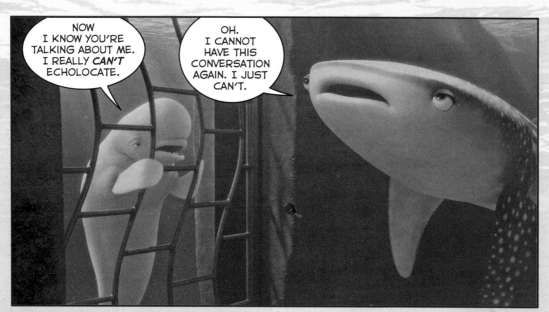

OPEN OCEAN. I-I'M PRETTY SURE IT'S, UH...THAT BUILDING OVER THERE THAT'S... ILL-DEFINED AND ROUNDISH. LIKE BAILEY'S HEAD.

WAIT, WHAT?

THERE'S ALWAYS ANOTHER WAY. THERE'S ALWAYS ANOTHER... ⸱GASP!⸱

THERE! GUYS, FOLLOW ME. I KNOW HOW I CAN GET TO LOCOMOTION!

OPEN OCEAN.

EXACTLY.

⸱SIGH⸱

CALLING "HER" OVER. CALLING WHO OVER?

A FLOCK OF LOONS LANDS NEARBY.

SPLASH SPLASH

LADS, MEET BECKY.

SQUAWK!

FLUKE POINTS TO THE QUARANTINE BUILDING.

LOOK, YOUR FRIEND IS GOING TO BE IN QUARANTINE. THAT'S WHERE THEY TAKE THE SICK FISH.

AND THE ONE--AND ONLY ONE--WAY INTO THAT PLACE...

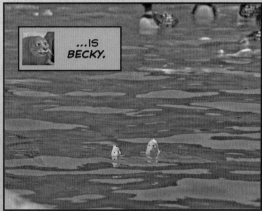

...IS BECKY.

SQUAWK!

AAH!

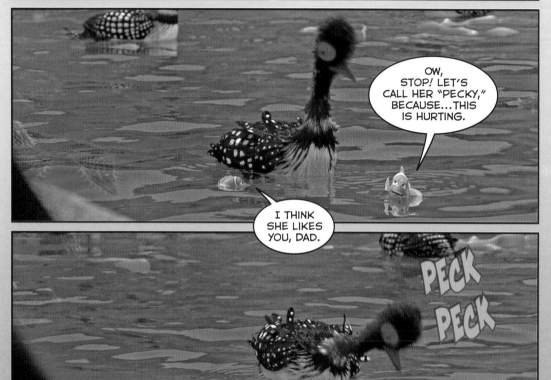

OW! SHE DOESN'T UNDERSTAND WHAT I'M SAYING.

ALL YOU HAVE TO DO IS *IMPRINT* WITH HER, MATE.

IMP-WHAT?

IMPRINT.

IMPRINT.

LOOK HER IN THE EYE AND SAY "OOO-ROO" AND SHE'LL BE IN SYNC WITH YOU.

⸓ORR-ROO!⸓

NOW, *LOOK HER IN THE EYE!*

YEAH!

NEMO...

I THINK WE SHOULD DEVISE AN ALTERNATE PLAN. ONE THAT INVOLVES STAYING IN THE WATER, AND SOMEONE SANE. BECAUSE THIS BIRD, THIS BIRD...THIS *AIN'T* THE BIRD!

THAT'S FINE, DAD. AND IN THE MEANTIME, DORY WILL JUST FORGET US. LIKE YOU SAID, IT'S *WHAT SHE DOES BEST.*

FINE.

⌒COO⌒

UH...OKAY. LOOK HER IN THE EYE.

WHICH... *WHICH EYE?*

JUST PICK ONE, MATE.

QUARANTINE

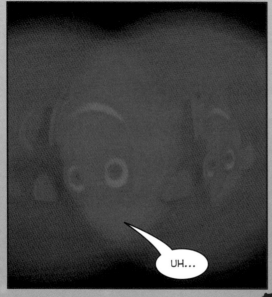

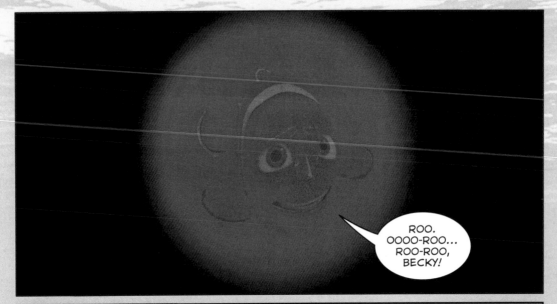

ROO. OOOO-ROO... ROO-ROO, BECKY!

SQUAAAAWK!

WITH THAT, BECKY HOPS ON TOP OF MARLIN!

COO

NO, NO.
THIS IS
NUTS!

WHY
DO I KEEP
GETTING TALKED
INTO INSANE
CHOICES?!

SQUAWK!

AAAAH!

GOOD LUCK!

OKAY, WHEN I TELL YOU, YOU'RE GONNA--

YEAH, I KNOW. I'M GONNA SIGNAL WITH A BIG SPLASH.

ON MY MARK. NOT CLEAR YET... NOT CLEAR YET...

FOLLOW THE SIGNS TO OPEN OCEAN...FOLLOW THE SIGNS TO OPEN OCEAN...

OVERLOOK
TIDAL TR
KELP CR
RESTROOMS
OPEN OCEAN
STROLLER PARKING

GO RIGHT!

SEEING THE SPILLED POPCORN, BECKY IMMEDIATELY CHANGES COURSE AND FLIES TO A TREE.

AS MARLIN YELLS TO BECKY, SOME OF THE WATER POURS OUT OF THE PAIL.

BECKY! BECKY?! OO-ROO!--

SUDDENLY, THE BRANCH SNAPS BACK, SENDING NEMO AND MARLIN FLYING THROUGH THE AIR!

WAAAUGH!

AUUUGH!

WAAH!

SPLASH

LOOKING FOR THE WORLD'S MOST POWERFUL PAIR OF GLASSES. LOOKING FOR THE WORLD'S MOST POWERFUL PAIR OF---;GASP; *OTTERS!*

IT'S A HUGE CUDDLE PARTY!

OOOOOOOOOOO!

CUDDLE PARTY! I'M IN!

WHERE ARE WE? ARE WE CLOSE TO OPEN OCEAN?

UH, YES...I THINK. WELL, I DON'T KNOW. BUT I SAW THAT OTHER SIGN, SO--

WHAT? WHAT OTHER SIGN?

AUGH!

HANK PULLS THEM OFF THE ROAD AND INTO THE SHADOWS BEHIND THE ROW OF TRASH CANS.

ALL RIGHT, THAT'S *IT!* YOU HAVE *WASTED* MY TIME!

WAIT, NO.

THAT TRANSPORT TRUCK LEAVES AT DAWN, AND I'M NOT MISSING IT! SO GIVE ME YOUR *TAG!*

WAIT-- NO, NO! I REMEMBERED THAT SIGN.

SO?!

THE STOLLER ROLLS BACKWARD, CRASHING INTO THE EDGE OF THE TOUCH POOL, AND LAUNCHING HANK AND DORY INTO ITS WATERS!

KERSPLOOSH

TOUCH POOL

I DID *NOT* LOSE THEM! HANK?...

HANK? *HANK?*

HANS...

HANK SCRAMBLES TO AN UNDERHANG BENEATH A ROCK AS DORY FOLLOWS.

HANK! *AAH!* W-WHAT'S THE PLAN?

THE PLAN IS I'M GONNA STAY HERE *FOREVER!*

O-OKAY. GOOD PLAN.

CHOOM

AAAH!

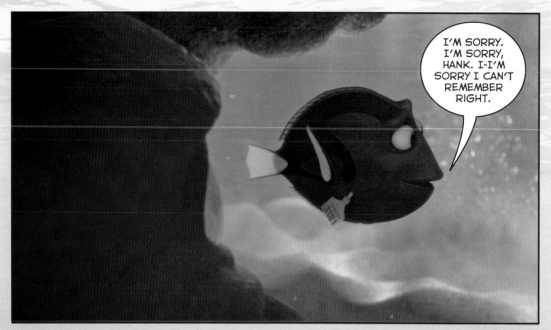

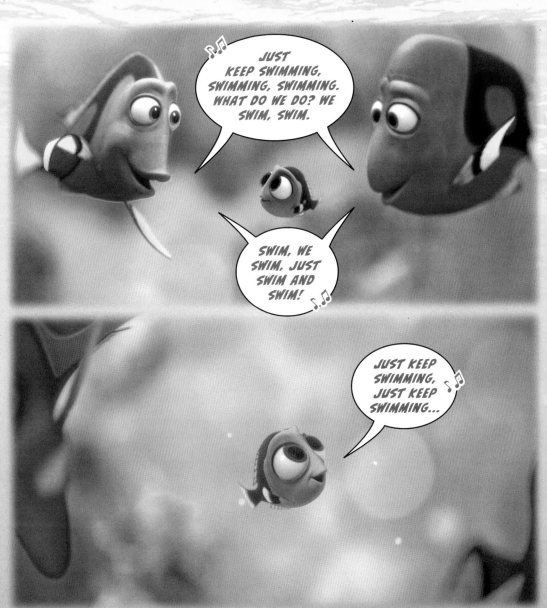

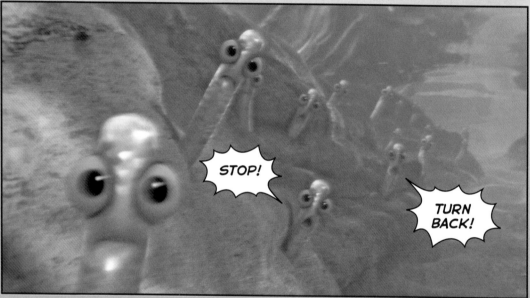

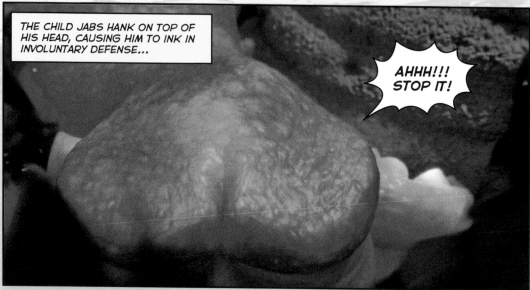

THE CHILD JABS HANK ON TOP OF HIS HEAD, CAUSING HIM TO INK IN INVOLUNTARY DEFENSE...

AHHH!!! STOP IT!

EW! WHAT IS IT?!

AHH!

EEEEK!

208

PLIP

HANK? OH, *HANK!* THERE YOU ARE!

:GASP!:

THE WORLD'S MOST POWERFUL PAIR OF GLASSES. *WE FOUND IT!*

NO, NO, NO. YOU FOUND *THAT.*

HELLO. WELCOME TO THE OPEN OCEAN!

HOME.

:·COO?·:

OO-ROO! OO-ROO! OO-ROO! OO-ROO! OO-ROO! OO-ROO! OO-ROO! OO-ROO! OO-ROO! **OO-ROO!** *OO-ROO! OO-ROO!*

DAD, STOP. SHE'S NOT COMING BACK.

SHE MIGHT. OO-ROO! OO-ROO!--

DAD! YOU MADE HER FEEL LIKE SHE *COULDN'T DO IT!*

YOU'RE NOT TALKING ABOUT *BECKY,* ARE YOU?

I MISS DORY.

ME TOO.

CLACKA-CLACKA-CLACKA-CLACK

THE TRUTH IS, I'M JUST SO *WORRIED* ABOUT HER.

SHE'S THE ONE WHO SHOULD BE WORRIED ABOUT *US.*

WELL, SHE WOULD DEFINITELY HAVE AN IDEA OF WHAT TO DO IF SHE WERE HERE. I DON'T KNOW HOW SHE DOES THAT.

I DON'T THINK SHE KNOWS, DAD. SHE JUST... DOES.

WHAT WOULD DORY DO?

WELL, THEN WE'LL JUST HAVE TO... THINK.

...WHAT *WOULD* DORY DO?

YEAH, WHAT WOULD DORY DO?!

SHE WOULD ASSESS HER SITUATION, AND THEN SHE'D EVALUATE. THEN, SHE WOULD ANALYZE HER OPTIONS--

DAD. THAT'S "WHAT WOULD MARLIN DO?"

RIGHT. THAT'S WHAT *I* WOULD DO. SHE WOULDN'T EVEN THINK TWICE. SHE WOULD JUST LOOK AT THE FIRST THING SHE SEES, AND--

BUMP BUMP BUMP

OUTSIDE, CHILDREN ARE PLAYING IN A "JUMPING FOUNTAIN" PLAZA. THE JETS OF WATER SHOOT OUT FROM HOLES IN A ZIG-ZAG PATTERN TOWARD...AN OUTDOOR TIDE POOL EXHIBIT.

HA HA HA!

TIDE

⊰SIGH⊱

DORY WOULD DO IT.

⊰HUP⊱ NEMO, HOLD ON TO ME! ⊰UNGHF⊱

THEY BOUNCE OFF THE TOP OF A STROLLER, AND...

WHOA! AHHH!

WOO HOO!

SPROING

HEY!
IT'S
WORKING!

...THEY'RE ONE JET STREAM AWAY FROM REACHING THE TIDAL POOL EXHIBIT WHEN...

...ALL THE JET STREAMS SHUT OFF.

MARLIN AND NEMO FLAP ON THE GROUND, HELPLESS AND EXPOSED, GASPING FOR WATER.

FLAP

♪ ⸫GASP!⸫ JUST... KEEP... GASPING...

⸫GASP!⸫

SUDDENLY, ALL OF THE JET STREAMS TURN ON AT ONCE! MARLIN AND NEMO ARE SHOT HIGH UP INTO THE AIR!

AAAAH!

FATHER AND SON SAIL THROUGH THE AIR AND LAND WITH A...

219

WELL, I WOULD LOVE TO, BUT MY SON AND I HAVE TO GET TO QUARANTINE SO--

OH, YEAH. IT IS.

'COURSE, I DON'T HAVE A FAMILY. I DATED A NICE SCALLOP FOR AWHILE.

WONDERFUL THING TO HAVE A SON.

BUT SCALLOPS HAVE EYES. AND SHE WAS LOOKING FOR SOMETHING DIFFERENT. I'M KIDDING! WELL, NOT ABOUT SCALLOPS HAVING EYES. THEY DO. AND THEY SEE INTO YOUR SOUL AND THEY BREAK YOUR HEART.

OH, SHELLEY. *WHHHHYYYYY?!* *WHHHHYYYYY?!*

NOW WHAT WOULD DORY DO?

COME WITH US, AS WE EXPLORE THE MYSTERIOUS WORLD OF THE OPEN OCEAN.

OKAY, HANK, FOLLOW ME.

YOU'RE IN A CUP.

RIGHT. I'LL FOLLOW YOU, THEN.

PANGEA

SHLUP

SHLUP

HANK MAKES HIS WAY ACROSS THE ROOM BY CLIMBING A CEILING BANNER...

...AND MAKING HIS WAY DOWN THE BACK OF A HANGING WHALE SCULPTURE.

AN OCTOPUS HAS THREE HEARTS

2 PUMP BLOOD TO THE GILLS, 1 PUMPS BLOOD THROUGHOUT THE BODY

WAIT--

AN OCTOPUS HAS THREE HEARTS.

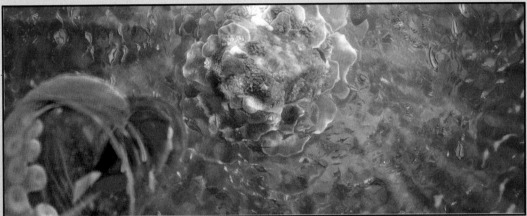

:CHUCKLE: TAG.

THE TAG. RIGHT.

YOU KNOW... I THINK I'M GOING TO REMEMBER YOU.

AH, YOU'LL FORGET ME IN A HEARTBEAT, KID. THREE HEARTBEATS.

I'LL HAVE A HARD TIME FORGETTING *YOU*, THOUGH.

MY PARENTS ARE ACTUALLY DOWN THERE.

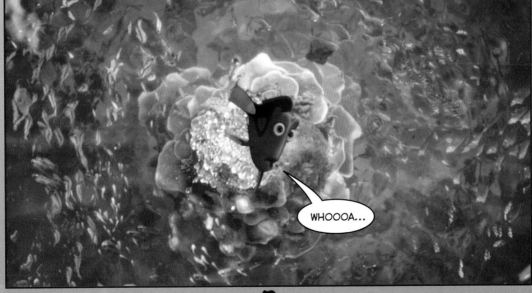

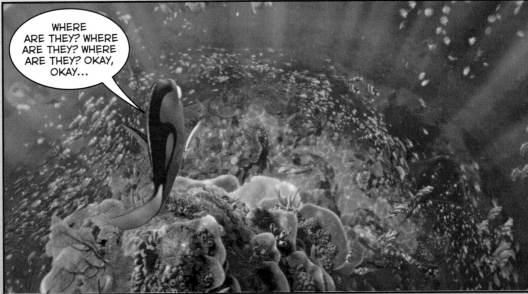

WHERE ARE THEY? WHERE ARE THEY? WHERE ARE THEY? OKAY, OKAY...

PARDON ME, AH, OH...

EXCUSE ME, HAVE YOU SEEN A COUPLE--THEY'RE OLD, LIKE YOU--NOT OLD LIKE YOU--BUT OLDER THAN YOU, EVEN.

OKAY. BYE!

HI! DO YOU KNOW ANYONE WHO LOST A KID...A LONG TIME AGO? THAT WOULD BE... ME?

I DON'T KNOW HOW LONG AGO, EXACT--

SPURRED ON BY THE MEMORY, DORY SWIMS FORWARD, FOLLOWING THE TRAIL OF SHELLS...

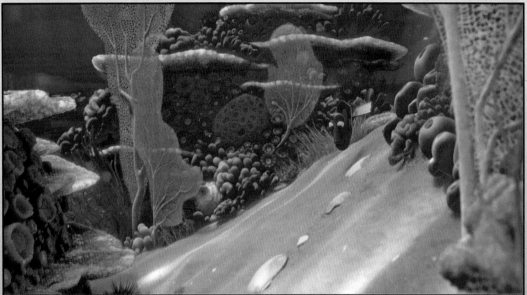

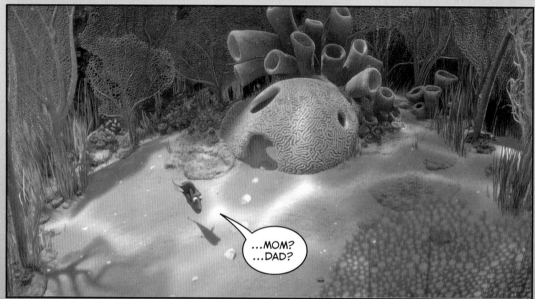

...MOM?
...DAD?

THEN, THROUGH AN OPENING IN THE GRASS, DORY SEES A PURPLE SHELL IN THE SAND.

OH NO. D-DON'T CRY, MOMMY. DON'T CRY...

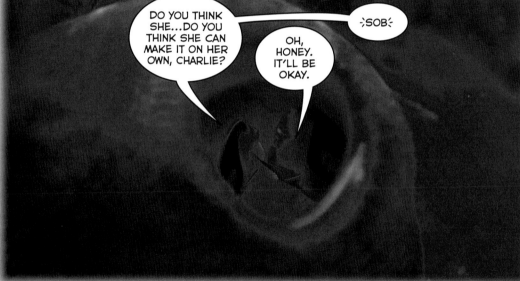

DO YOU THINK SHE...DO YOU THINK SHE CAN MAKE IT ON HER OWN, CHARLIE?

OH, HONEY. IT'LL BE OKAY.

⊰SOB⊱

LITTLE DORY LOOKS AROUND DESPERATELY UNTIL SHE SEES A PURPLE SHELL IN THE DISTANCE.

MOMMY?

SUDDENLY, DORY IS PULLED INTO THE UNDERTOW!

AHHHH!

DORY!!!

DORY!!!

OH NO. IT'S HAPPENING. OKAY, HOLD ON, HOLD ON, HOLD ON, HOLD ON...

DORY SWIMS DOWN ANOTHER PIPE AND TAKES A LEFT, THEN A RIGHT.

WHICH WAY? WHERE AM I GOING? I CAN'T REMEMBER.

OKAY. OKAY. I'M LOST. IT'S TOO HARD. I CAN'T REMEMBER. I'M FORGETTING EVERYTHING! I'M GONNA BE STUCK FOREVER IN THE PIPES! *THE PIPES!* THE PIPE PALS. PIPE PALS? *PIPE PALS!*

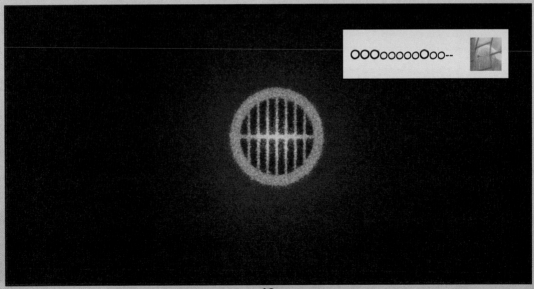

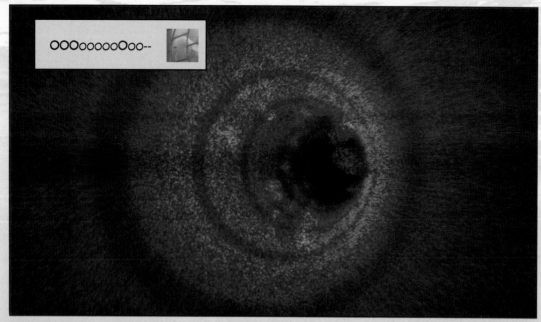

OOOoooooOoo--

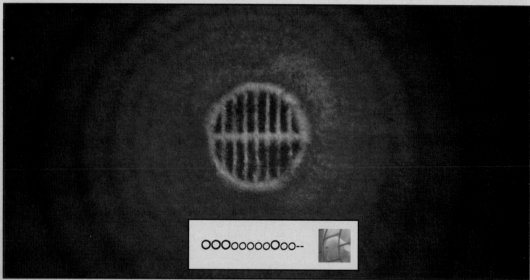

OOOooooooOoo--

OOOooooooOoo--
HERE WE GO!
OoooooOoo--*OH YES!*
OOooo--*I CAN SEE
THE QUARANTINE!*

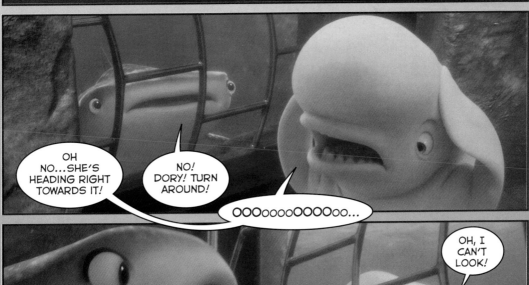

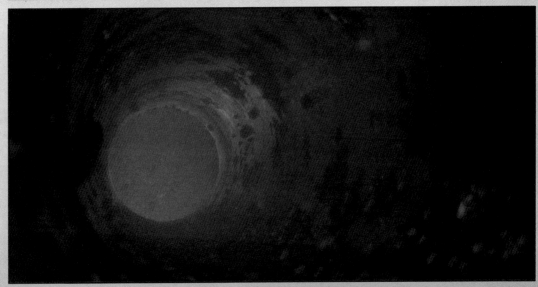

AS THE SUN SETS, TOURISTS EXIT THE PARK AND STAFFERS BEGIN THE PROCESS OF CLOSING THE INSTITUTE FOR THE NIGHT.

VRRRRRM

AT THE QUARANTINE LOADING DOCK, STAFFERS LINE UP TANKS TO LOAD ONTO A WAITING TRANSPORT TRUCK.

HEY, SO HOW MUCH MORE WE GOT LEFT TO LOAD?

UH, JUST THIS LAST ROW.

THE SOONER WE FINISH, THE SOONER THIS TRUCK GETS TO CLEVELAND.

WATCH THE TURN!

WATCH WHAT?

THUD

OW.

TOO LATE.

OKAY, I THINK WE'RE CLOSE.

DORY, MARLIN, AND NEMO FALL OUT OF THE PIPE AND INTO A TANK BELOW.

HI!

IS THIS QUARANTINE?

YES! THIS IS IT! WE'RE IN QUARANTINE! *MY PARENTS ARE HERE!*

SUDDENLY, THE ENTIRE TANK STARTS TO MOVE AS A WORKER PUSHES THEIR TANK TOWARD A DOOR.

YAAAAY!

WHERE ARE WE GOING? HEY, WHA-- NO, NO, WHY ARE WE GOING TOWARDS THE DOOR?

WE'RE ALL BETTER!

YAAAAY!

I FEEL FANTASTIC!

∴AH-CHOO!∴

-:GASP!:-

DUDE.

THE YELLOW FISH ASIDE, DORY LOOKS OUT BEYOND THE TANK AND SEES...

...A TANK FULL OF BLUE TANGS!

MY FAMILY! C'MON, LET'S GO!

EXCUSE ME...

DORY, WAIT A MINUTE!

I'M COMING MOMMY! I'M COMING DADDY! WOO HOO!

MARLIN AND NEMO FOLLOW DORY AS SHE LEAPS FROM TANK TO TANK, TOWARD THE AQUARIUM FULL OF BLUE TANGS...

ALMOST HOME...ALMOST HOME...I'M ALMOST HOME...

HA HA HA!

I THINK I'M GETTING THE HANG OF THIS!

SPLASH!

BUT SUDDENLY, ONE OF THE TANKS IS LIFTED UP BY THE STAFF TO BE LOADED ONTO THE TRUCK...

SPLAT

...SENDING DORY, MARLIN, AND NEMO SPLASHING INTO THE NEARBY MOP BUCKET!

SPLOOSH

WET FLOOR

I HEAR FOOTSTEPS!

AHHHH!

GASP GASP

GASP

HANK DROPS THE THREE FISH INTO A CONTAINER OF WATER.

HANK!

QUIET.

HANK, WE NEED TO GET IN THAT TANK.

THAT RHYMED!

HANK LOWERS THE THREE FISH INTO THE TANK OF BLUE TANGS.

MOM? DAD?

MOM? DAD? HEY EVERYBODY, IT'S ME, DORY.

DORY?... DORY?!...

DORY? DORY? DORY?

IS IT REALLY HER?...

YOU MEAN THE LITTLE FORGETFUL FISH?...

I CAN'T BELIEVE IT...

IT'S DORY!... DORY!...

OH, IT'S JENNY AND CHARLIE'S GIRL.

MOM? DAD?

WHERE ARE MY PARENTS?

OH NO.

DORY? ARE YOU REALLY JENNY AND CHARLIE'S GIRL?

YES, I AM! THAT'S ME! WHERE ARE THEY?!

UH... WELL, DORY...RIGHT AFTER YOU DISAPPEARED, THEY THOUGHT YOU...WELL, THEY THOUGHT YOU MUST HAVE ENDED UP HERE, IN QUARANTINE.

UH-HUH?

OUTSIDE THE TANK, HANK WATCHES AS THEY START TO LOAD TANKS ONTO THE TRUCK.

C'MON, C'MON, C'MON.

THEY *WANTED* TO FIND YOU.

ARE YOU SURE? ARE YOU SURE THEY'RE GONE?

DORY, LISTEN, IT'S GOING TO BE OKAY.

DORY'S HEART BEGINS TO RACE, HER VISION BEGINS TO BLUR.

OH, DORY, THEY LOVED YOU SO *MUCH.*

ANYONE NOT LOOKING TO GO TO CLEVELAND, FINAL WARNING!

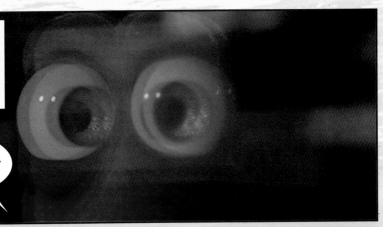

HANK WATCHES THE FORKLIFT GO UNDER THE TANK AND QUICKLY SCOOPS UP DORY, MISSING MARLIN AND NEMO.

WHERE'S EVERYBODY ELSE?

⁖GASP⁖

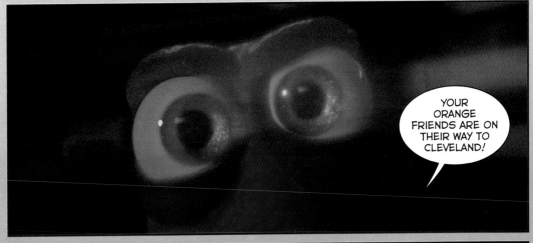

YOUR ORANGE FRIENDS ARE ON THEIR WAY TO CLEVELAND!

SUDDENLY, A GIANT HAND GRABS HANK AND HE DROPS DORY.

GAAAH!

GOTCHA! I FOUND THE OCTOPUS!

HANK SLAPS THE STAFFER AND SCURRIES TOWARD A NEARBY TANK TO CAMOUFLAGE.

AAH!

WHERE DID HE GO?

DORY SPILLS OUT ONTO THE FLOOR AND FALLS...

AHH! MOMMY! DADDY!

...INTO A DRAIN THAT LEADS TO THE OCEAN.

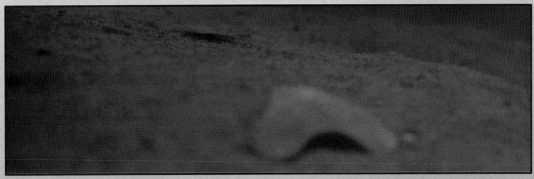

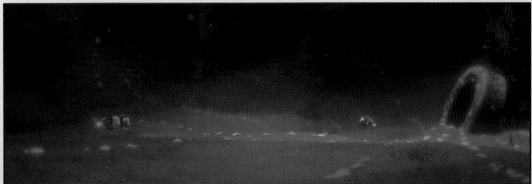

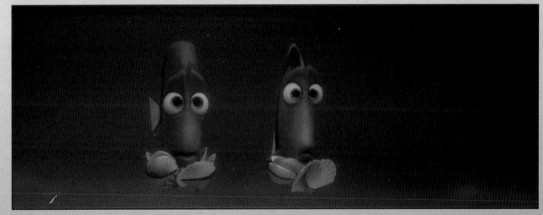

DORY!

DORY!

HA HA HA! YOU'RE HERE. YOU'RE REALLY HERE. YOU FOUND US...MY MISSING GIRL... YOU'RE HERE. LOOK AT YOU...

OH, MY BABY! LET ME LOOK AT YOU. I'M NEVER LETTING YOU GO AGAIN. MY BABY!

AND *YOU* FOUND US. OH, HONEY, YOU FOUND US... AND YOU KNOW WHY YOU FOUND US? BECAUSE YOU REMEMBERED. YOU *REMEMBERED* IN YOUR OWN, AMAZING, DORY WAY.

I DID. ALL BY MYSELF.

OH, HONEY. REALLY? HAVE YOU BEEN...BY YOURSELF ALL THESE YEARS?

OH, MY POOR LITTLE GIRL.

OH, I HAVEN'T BEEN ALL BY MYSELF--

MARLIN AND NEMO!

DORY IS RACING BACK, TALKING A MILE A MINUTE TO HER PARENTS.

☆HUFF HUFF☆

AND THEN THE WHALE SWALLOWED US-- EVEN THOUGH I SPEAK WHALE.

A WHALE?!

GOOD THING I WASN'T THERE TO SEE THAT.

ACTUALLY, MARLIN NEVER BELIEVES I EVEN KNOW HOW TO SPEAK WHALE, BUT YOU KNOW, HE ALWAYS KINDA TRUSTS ME ANYWAY.

YOU KNOW, I LIKE THIS MARLIN ALREADY!

YEAH. AND THEN SOMEHOW WE FOUND NEMO--OR DID HE FIND ME? I DON'T KNOW, BUT YOU KNOW WHAT? NEMO IS JUST THE SWEETEST...

HE JUST NEVER GIVES UP ON ME. NO MATTER WHAT.

303

DESTINY SWIMS TOWARD THE WALL AT FULL SPEED!

WHAT? NO! DESTINY, WAIT! NO! *THAT'S A WALL! WALL!*

AAAH!

DESTINY LEAPS...

AAAH!

AAAH!

AAAH!

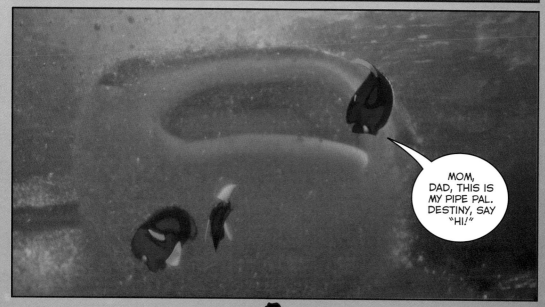

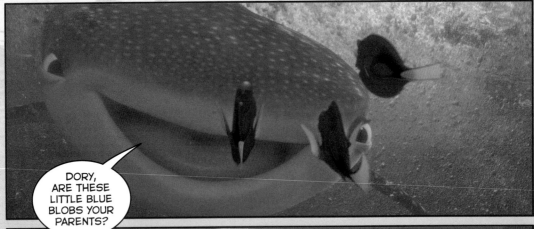

DORY, ARE THESE LITTLE BLUE BLOBS YOUR PARENTS?

THEY LOOK JUST LIKE YOU!

SPLOOSH

HELLO, I'M BAILEY. MRS. DORY, MR. DORY...

OH, PLEASE! CALL ME JENNY.

OH, AND I'M CHARLIE.

OKAY, OKAY. WE GOTTA GO! WE GOTTA STOP THAT TRUCK!

DORY AND HER PARENTS GRAB HOLD OF ONE OF DESTINY'S FINS AND SHE TAKES OFF.

BAILEY! I FORGOT EVERYTHING! CATCH ME UP!

YES, MA'AM! OOOOOOOOOooooo....

YOUR FRIENDS ARE STILL ON THE TRUCK! OOOOoo-- THEY'RE HEADED NORTH TOWARDS THE BRIDGE! OOOOoo--

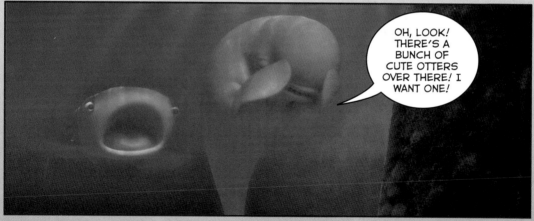

OH, LOOK! THERE'S A BUNCH OF CUTE OTTERS OVER THERE! I WANT ONE!

OW!

AGH!

DORY, SWEETIE? WHAT HAPPENS IF...YOU KNOW, IF...IF...YOU'RE GONE FOR...I MEAN TOO LONG... AND YOU GET CONFUSED... AND THAT MAKES YOU DISTRACTED, AND WHAT IF--

MOM... MOM... MOM...

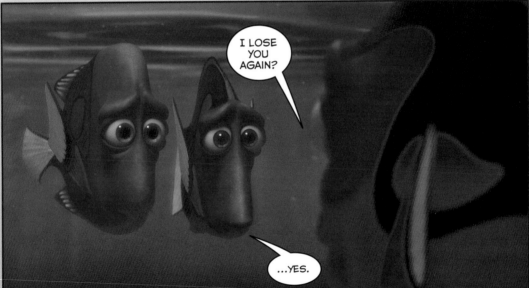

I LOSE YOU AGAIN?

...YES.

MOM. DAD. IT'S GONNA BE OKAY...

...BECAUSE I KNOW THAT EVEN IF I FORGET...

...I CAN FIND YOU AGAIN.

OOOO-- OKAY, A LITTLE LEFT...OOOOOOO-- BACK THE OTHER WAY A BIT. OOOO--OKAY, THAT'S IT. GO! *DON'T DO IT!*

OKAY, NOW! NOW! DO IT! *DO IT!*

BAILEY!

TIME FOR YOUR IDEA.

OKAY, WHAT IDEA?

WAAAAAAAAAH!

STOP TRAFFIC! CUDDLE PARTY!

SCREEEEEECH!

AAH!

HEY!

WHAT'S GOING ON, DAD?

WHAT...?

I DON'T KNOW HOW, I DON'T KNOW IN WHAT WAY...BUT I THINK THIS HAS SOMETHING TO DO WITH--

DORY!

WATER... WATER... I NEED WATER...

HANK REACHES DOWN, AND MOVES TO PLACE DORY IN THE TANK WITH MARLIN AND NEMO.

ARE YOU *CRAZY?!* HOW'D YOU GET HERE?

HEY...

DORY!

I THOUGHT WE'D NEVER SEE YOU AGAIN.

AW, ME TOO. BUT DARN IT, NO MATTER HOW HARD I TRIED, I JUST COULDN'T FORGET YOU. GUESS I MISSED THE REST OF MY FAMILY TOO MUCH, HUH?

:GASP:

HEY!
HEY! COME ON.
OUT OF THE TRUCK.
THOSE AREN'T YOUR
FISH. SHOO!

OH, NO, THERE
GOES OUR
RIDE!

DOOORY!
THE TRAFFIC
IS STARTING TO
MOOOOOOVE!

DORY, FOLLOW ME!

MARLIN AND NEMO HOP INTO THE PAIL, BUT BECKY TAKES OFF WITHOUT DORY!

NO, NO, *WAIT!* WE DON'T HAVE *DORY!* NO, NO, BECKY, WAIT!

STOP IT! WE NEED TO GO *BACK!* BECKY! *BACK! BACK,* BECKY! OO-ROO! *OOO-ROO-OO-ROO!*

PLISH

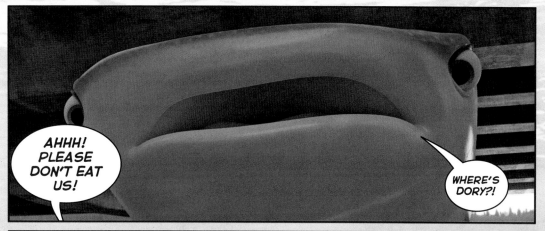

WITH THAT, BECKY TAKES OFF AND FLIES TO THE BACK OF THE TRUCK.

SQUAWK! SQUAWK!

OKAY, KID. I GUESS THIS IS GOOD-BYE.

SLAP

NO!

WHADDYA MEAN, "NO?"

I MEAN, YOU'RE NOT GOING TO CLEVELAND. YOU ARE COMING TO THE OCEAN WITH ME.

WHAT *IS IT* WITH YOU AND RUINING MY PLANS? LISTEN TO ME, I HAVE ONE GOAL IN LIFE, ONE! AND IT IS TO--

WHAT IS SO GREAT ABOUT PLANS? I'VE NEVER HAD A PLAN. DID I PLAN TO LOSE MY PARENTS? NO. DID I PLAN TO FIND MARLIN? NO. DID YOU AND I PLAN TO MEET?

NO, *YOU* LISTEN TO *ME!*

WAIT... DID WE?

ARE YOU ALMOST DONE?

WELL,
I DON'T *THINK* WE DID,
AND THAT'S BECAUSE THE
BEST THINGS HAPPEN BY
CHANCE, BECAUSE THAT'S
LIFE, AND THAT'S YOU
BEING WITH ME, OUT IN THE
OCEAN, NOT SAFE IN SOME
STUPID GLASS
BOX.

CAN I SAY
SOMETHING?

I'M
NOT DONE!
A VOICE ONCE TOLD ME
THAT ALL IT TAKES IS
THREE SIMPLE STEPS--
RESCUE, REHABILITATION,
AND...

...UM...
ONE OTHER
THING
THAT...

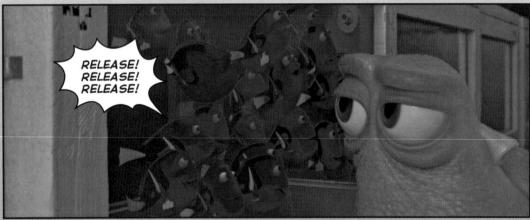

DESTINY SWIMS FULL SPEED AHEAD WITH DORY'S PARENTS, MARLIN, NEMO, AND BAILEY.

OoOOOOooooOO--

OoOOOOooooOO--HE'S TRYING TO GET THE DOOR OPEN! OOOO-- IT'S LOCKED FROM THE OUTSIDE!

DORY... IT'S OVER.

RATTLE RATTLE

NO, T-THERE'S GOTTA BE A WAY.

YEAH! THERE'S A WAY!

DORY, NOW LISTEN TO ME. THERE'S NO WAY TO GET OUT.

WELL, WHAT ABOUT THAT?

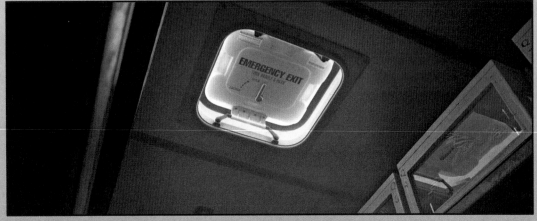

HOLY CARP. THERE IS ANOTHER WAY.

TAKE A DEEP BREATH, KID.

YAAAY!

AAAH! GET IT OFF! WHAT IS THAT?! WHAT IS THAT?! GET IT OFF! WHAT IS IT?

SPLOP

USDOT 379385688
GVW 26,000

CALA113

SCREEEECH

WHAT THE--?

MARINE LIFE INSTITUTE
CLEVELAND

SLAM

CALA113

HANK CLOSES THE TRUCK DOORS AND LOCKS THEM!

CHUNK

HEH. SUCK IT, BIPEDS!

ALL RIGHT, HANK. YOU'VE GOT SEVEN ARMS, JUST-- I DUNNO. TRY SOMETHING!

HEH HEH! HERE WE GO.

HOOONK

KRRRNK

HANK GRABS THE GEAR SHIFT AND PUTS THE TRUCK IN DRIVE.

LISTEN. I'M NOT TELLING YOU HOW TO DRIVE. CERTAINLY I CAN'T-- I'M NOT IN ANY POSITION...BUT COULD YOU GO FASTER?

UH...

HANK TRIES A PEDAL. IT'S THE GAS! THE TRUCK SURGES FORWARD.

WOO-HOO!

WAAAH!

VROOOOM

HEY! GIVE US OUR TRUCK BACK!

I CAN'T SEE SQUAT! WHICH WAY ARE WE GOING?

OKAY, WELL, UM... ALL THE CARS ARE GOING LEFT, SO... SO GO LEFT!

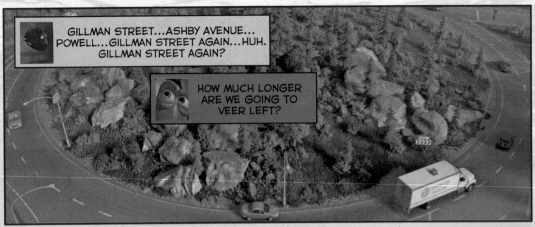

GILLMAN STREET...ASHBY AVENUE... POWELL...GILLMAN STREET AGAIN...HUH. GILLMAN STREET AGAIN?

HOW MUCH LONGER ARE WE GOING TO VEER LEFT?

IT'S OKAY. WE JUST NEED TO KNOW HOW WE GOT ON AND THEN WE'LL KNOW HOW TO GET OFF.

WELL, LET ME KNOW WHEN YOU FIGURE IT OUT!

UNFORTUNATELY, I CAN'T REMEMBER HOW WE GOT ON.

HAVING MADE A COMPLETE CIRCLE, HANK AND DORY PASS THE DISTRAUGHT MLI STAFFERS.

HEY! HEEEEEY!

STOP! HEEEY!

HEY, I KNOW THOSE GUYS. THAT'S WHERE WE CAME FROM. TURN RIGHT!

SCREEEEEECH

HERE WE GO!

HEY!

WE ARE SO FIRED!

SCREEEECH

KEEP STRAIGHT! STRAIGHT... LEFT! LEFT! NO, NO, NO, NO. RIGHT, RIGHT, RIGHT!

GOOD DRIVING, HANK!

PAY ATTENTION TO THE ROAD!

HANK TURNS THE TRUCK OFF ONE FREEWAY AND ONTO ANOTHER.

HANK SEES THAT THE GAS TANK IS ALMOST EMPTY.

UM, WELL...OKAY, I'LL FIGURE IT OUT. I DON'T KNOW, BUT, WELL SOMETHING WILL COME AND, UM--

WE'RE OUT OF TIME, KID! WHERE DO WE GO NOW?

OOOOOOO-- UH-OH... IT'S THE FUZZ. BUSTED!

WEEEOOOO WEEEOOOO WEEEOOOO

WEEEOOOO WEEEOOOO WEEEOOOO

OKAY, WE'RE GOOD.

THE OCEAN! IT'S STRAIGHT AHEAD! *FLOOR IT!*

NOW WE'RE TALKING.

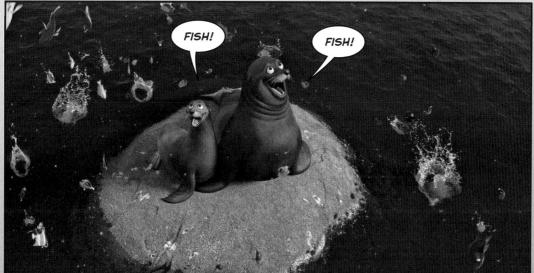

SPLOOSH

THANK YOU
FOR JOINING
ME.

ONE, TWO, THREE, FOUR...UH...WAIT A MINUTE. WHY AM I COUNTING?

HEY, WHERE IS EVERYONE? UH-OH. DID...DID THEY LEAVE ME?

NO. NO, NO, THEY WOULDN'T DO THAT.

OKAY, THAT'S OKAY, I CAN FIGURE THIS OUT. WHAT WAS I DOING JUST THEN? I WAS UM... COVERING MY FACE... SO I WAS TRYING TO HIDE.

OKAY, SO WHY WAS I TRYING TO HIDE? WAIT! OH, I'M--

FIVE, SIX, SEVEN, EIGHT, NINE, TEN!

READY OR NOT, HERE I COME!

HA! FOUND YOU!

HA HA HA!

I SEE YOU!

OH!

WHOA!

HA HA! GOTCHA!

HA HA HA HA!

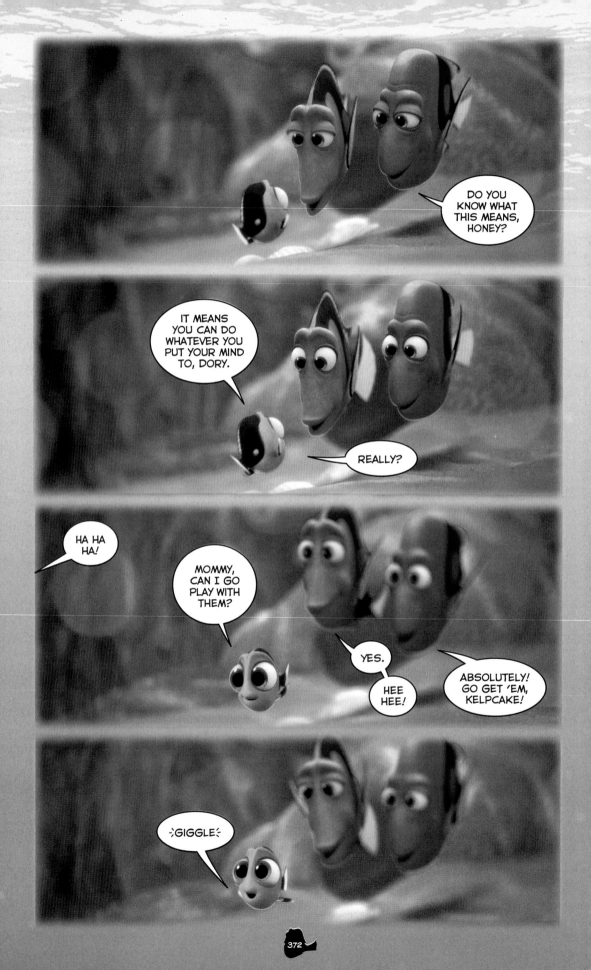

DIRECTOR
Andrew Stanton

CO-DIRECTOR
Angus MacLane

PRODUCER
Lindsey Collins

ORIGINAL STORY BY
Andrew Stanton

SCREENPLAY BY
Andrew Stanton
Victoria Strouse

ADDITIONAL SCREENPLAY MATERIAL BY
Bob Peterson

ADDITIONAL STORY MATERIAL BY
Angus MacLane